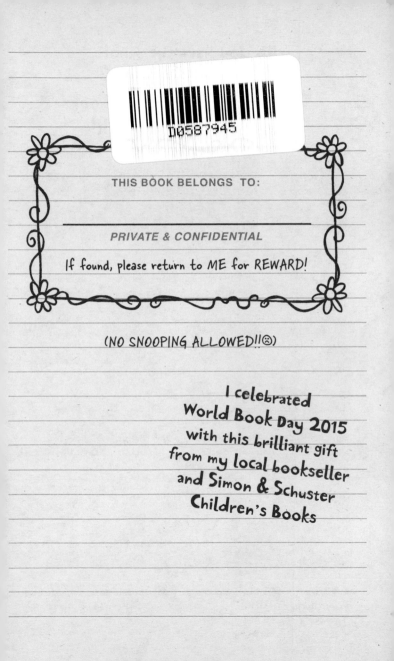

THIS BOOK BELONGS TO:

PRIVATE & CONFIDENTIAL

If found, please return to ME for REWARD!

(NO SNOOPING ALLOWED!!☺)

I celebrated
World Book Day 2015
with this brilliant gift
from my local bookseller
and Simon & Schuster
Children's Books

Rachel Renée Russell

DORK diaries

OMG

How to be a DORK!

SIMON AND SCHUSTER

First published in Great Britain in 2015 by Simon and Schuster UK Ltd
A CBS COMPANY

This book has been specially written and published for World Book Day 2015. For further information, visit www.worldbookday.com. World Book Day in the UK and Ireland is made possible by generous sponsorship from National Book Tokens, participating publishers, authors, illustrators and booksellers. Booksellers who accept the £1* World Book Day Book Token bear the full cost of redeeming it.

World Book Day, **World Book Night** and **Quick Reads** are annual initiatives designed to encourage everyone in the UK and Ireland — whatever your age — to read more and discover the joy of books and reading for pleasure. **World Book Night** is a celebration of books and reading for adults and teens on 23 April, which sees book gifting and celebrations in thousands of communities around the country: www. worldbooknight.org **Quick Reads** provides brilliant short new books by bestselling authors to engage adults in reading: www.quickreads.org.uk

*€1.50 in Ireland

1 3 5 7 9 10 8 6 4 2

Simon & Schuster UK Ltd, 1st Floor, 222 Gray's Inn Road, London WC1X 8HB

A CIP catalogue record for this book is available from the British Library.

PB ISBN: 978-1-4711-2448-8

Printed and bound by CPI Group (UK) Ltd, Croydon, CRO 4YY

www.simonandschuster.co.uk
www.dorkdiaries.co.uk

Hello fellow Dorks!

OMG I am SO excited to share this extra special, dorktastic World Book Day book with you guys! This book is filled with EVERYTHING you'll ever need to know about embracing your dorky side including: coping with crushes, avoiding BFF dramas, planning adorkable parties, surviving family "fun" days, discovering YOUR style and, of course, how to write your very own dork diary!

Follow my hints and tips, answer the quizzes and read all about my cringe-worthy life — including some special diary entries you might not have seen before! — and you can become a fully-fledged dork just like me! And, most importantly, remember that being a dork is all about being yourself, because YOU are awesome, so always let your inner dork shine through!

Your guide-through-dorkdom,
Nikki Maxwell
☺

CONTENTS

page 1
EMBRACING YOUR INNER DORK

page 13
BFFS AND FRENEMIES

page 29
CRUSHES AND TOTAL RCS BOYS!

page 43
FAMILY DRAMA-RAMAS

page 53
SCHOOL'S OUT!

page 71
WHAT'S A DORK TO DO?

page 89
HOW TO WRITE YOUR OWN DORK DIARY

EMBRACING YOUR INNER DORK

PLEDGE ALLEGIANCE TO YOUR INNER DORK!

Being a true dork is something I know a lot about! If you want to be adorkable and dorkalicious then here are three rules that you should always try and follow:

1) Always remember to have fun!

This is number one on my list because it's SO important! I have the MOST fun hanging out with Zoey and Chloe, making up dances and being silly together. What do YOU do to have fun? Hang out with your BFFs? Read your fave books? Create music? Draw? Whatever it is, make sure you do it as often as you can!

2) Always respect and love your best pals!

Your BFFs are the ones who know you best, and it's important to make time for them and not create too much drama! I fight with Zoey and Chloe sometimes, but we know we'll be there for each other when it counts. Give your BFFs a big hug the next time you see them and show them just how awesome they are!

3) Embrace your inner dork and be true to yourself!
Never be afraid to be who you are; the crazy, silly and
weird things about your personality are what make YOU
amazing! I'm like a total klutz and nearly always say the
wrong thing, but that's just me. Don't try and change
yourself to fit in with everyone else, celebrate the things
that make you different and be proud of who you are!

GET YOUR BOOGIE ON AND GET HAPPY DANCING!

OMG!!!! Sometimes I'm SO super happy that I can't get a single word out of my huge, smiling mouth without giggling like a total dork! And I get CRAZY energy when I'm in a good mood, like I just ate 50 bags of sweets! When this happens, there's only one way to let out my inner happy: my extra special, totally secret snoopy happy dance! Feeling too excited for words? You don't need them! Follow these instructions and you too can look like a MASSIVE dork doing my snoopy happy dance. I hope you've got your leg warmers ready!

1) Put your hands
    behind your back

2) Jump up in the air
    and kick your feet
    backwards and forwards
    quickly. Repeat while you . . .

3) Lift both your hands
   in the air above your head

4) SMILE!

5) Spread your arms
   out to the side

6) SQUEEE!

7) Repeat until your
   happy is shared
   with the world!

Not feeling happy? Then
you REALLY need these
instructions! Studies show
that 99 out of 100 dorks felt instantly better after
just two minutes of snoopy happy dancing. (Okay, so
I made that up, but it always works for me!) So put
on your fave song and dance your worries away — and
remember: being a dork is about being silly sometimes, so
dance like no one's watching!

WHY DORKS MAKE THE BEST FRIENDS

Dorks are cool — fact! And there's nothing cooler than being a good friend, so it's no surprise that dorks make the best friends. Here's a list that I came up with of the reasons why it's great to be friends with people as dorky as you . . .

1) A dork will never be too cool to sit with you after you trip or say something embarrassing in front of everybody.

REALLY! A dork wouldn't make it worse by being all like, "I'm SO much cooler than you because I have perfect balance and communication skills!" Nope! A dork would totally have your back! If a friend tripped on a banana peel and it seemed like everyone was laughing and pointing in slow motion, like in a really bad movie, you know what I'd say? "Nothing to see here! Please disperse!" like I was a cop telling people to haul out instead of gawking at a really bad car accident. And why? Because dorks make awesome friends!

2) Dorks aren't afraid to be silly.

Think about the snobbiest CCP girl in
your school. I know . . . it hurts . . .
but it's just for a second, I promise!
Right, got her face in your head? Now
think about the last time you saw her
balancing a cherry on her nose while
patting her head and rubbing her belly?
I once did it for a whole five minutes,
beating an entire table of laughing dorks
in the lunchroom. Dorks don't care if
they look dumb, and that makes them
awesome friends!

3) Dorks are SUPER nice!

A dork will NEVER trip you, trap you in your locker, or
insult your clothes in front of your whole class with some
nasty comment. Dorks are nice to EVERYONE, even people
who act like they own the world (mentioning no names
cough MacKenzie Hollister *cough*)! Case in point:
Mackenzie walked into gym class yelling at some new girl

for sitting on HER spot on the bleachers, and the whole time she had a big strand of toilet paper hanging from her skirt! So, even though she's SUPERmean, I tried to tell her because, OMG how embarrassing . . . but of course she ignored me because she's afraid she'll catch dorkiness if she gets too close. After that, I just MIGHT have laughed so hard that I snorted. But, hey I tried to warn her!

4) Dorks will rule the world someday.

Let's face it: your dorkiest friend will probably invent the new Facebook or Twitter or Instagram. And in the meantime, she'll figure out how to make her own iPad for long nights of the NEW GGGing . . . giggling, gossiping, and GAMING! And why? Because dorks are super smart and AWESOME . . . and they make the best friends!!

ARE YOU PROUD TO BE DORK?

So how much of a dork are YOU? Take my fun quiz and find out...

1) Your fave TV show is something old and mega embarrassing, but you love sitting down and watching it with your grandma! The mean girl at school finds out about your secret TV love. What do you do?

a) Don't worry, everyone knows about your cringe-worthy TV show—your fave shirt has the show's logo on it!

b) Say nothing and hope that the gossip dies down, until you realize the most popular girl in class loves the show too and you can fangirl together!

c) Take a survey to see what everyone else watches so you can say, "OMG, I love those shows too! I only watch that other lame show with my grandmother because she makes me. Old people are so weird!"

2) What's your favorite thing to do when you're hanging out with your friends?

    a) Anything as long as all your BFFs are together and having fun!

    b) Hanging out watching movies together—although only if someone else chooses what you watch. You wouldn't want to pick the wrong thing!

    c) Go to the mall, where all the cool kids hang out (even though you'd much rather put on your Elsa dress and belt out "Let It Go").

3) What section do you always head for straight away in the school library?

    a) Comics and sci-fi section—no questions!

    b) Wherever everyone else is looking. That's where the best books will be.

    c) The magazine section, where you can read all about what the latest trends are. Sure, the library's full of interesting books, and you'll read them all . . . one day when you're popular!

4) Your favorite song comes on at the school disco. Do you head straight for the dance floor?

    a) Definitely! It's your time to shine!

b) Totally—unless your friends don't want to dance, and then you wait until they hit the floor.

c) No way! Your favorite song is totally lame, and the idea of dancing in public makes you so nervous that you almost pee a little thinking about it.

Mostly As: You're Dorky and Proud! You're not afraid to be yourself and have fun, no matter how it looks. Rock on, girlfriend, and remember: you're an inspiration to dorks around the world!

Mostly Bs: You're a Social Dork. You listen to your inner dork but you sometimes stress about what other people think. Newsflash: they're all worried about other people's opinions, too! So show them by example that it's okay to be their dorky selves. You'll ALL have a lot more fun that way!

Mostly Cs: You're an Undercover Dork! You hide your true self because you want to fit in, but your inner dork is DYING to get out! So try not to worry so much about looking cool, because you're missing out on all the stuff you love, and the world's missing out on the totally awesome real you!

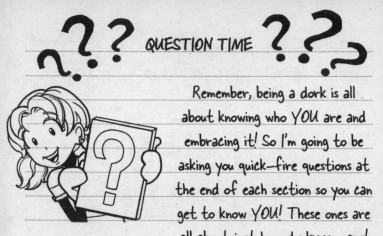

QUESTION TIME

Remember, being a dork is all about knowing who YOU are and embracing it! So I'm going to be asking you quick-fire questions at the end of each section so you can get to know YOU! These ones are all about just how dorky you are!

Why should YOU be crowned Princess of the Dorks?

Have you ever been so embarrassed that you wanted to dig a deep hole and crawl into it? Details, please!

If your life was a book, what would the title be and why?

If you could put your favorite motto or saying on a T-shirt, what would it say?

Which of your friends is as dorky as you? Why?

What's your biggest dorky secret?

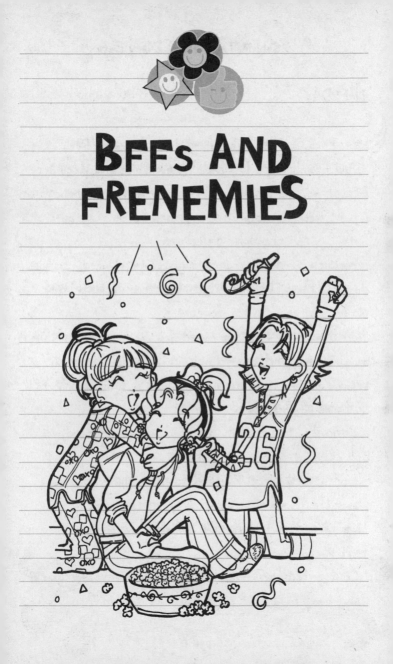

Shhh Top Secret Diary Entry!

TUESDAY

I am THIS CLOSE to breaking down in tears!!! ☹

And I don't cry a lot. But I think Chloe and Zoey are mad at me, and it's all over this huge misunderstanding!

Last weekend we were all supposed to hang out on Saturday and then have a sleepover.

We didn't really have anything specific planned for the day, but I was SUPERexcited about the sleepover. We always have so much fun together!!

That morning, Brandon called and asked me to help him at the animal shelter, and he said it was an emergency because his grandmother was sick, and if I didn't help, he'd be there all by himself.

Obviously I had to help. It's what any good friend would do!!

Since I knew Chloe, Zoey, and I didn't have anything planned, AND we were going to spend the whole night together, I didn't think they'd mind if I bailed on the first part.

So I texted them both: "Huge animal shelter emergency!! Can't hang today, but can't wait for tonight!!"

I had SO MUCH fun at the shelter, like I always do with Brandon and those cute little puppies!

But I forgot to check my phone until about 5pm. And BOTH Chloe and Zoey had texted me!

Zoey wrote: "Oh no! Maybe we can come help?? We have a HUGE surprise for you, and it's really important!"

And Chloe wrote: "I get it, a crush in need! As long as you can make it by 4pm!!"

They had called me a few times too, but I'd had my phone on vibrate.

Before I even checked my voicemails, I wrote back to both of them superfast: "Sorry! I just saw your text! What time for the sleepover tonight?"

Then Zoey wrote back: "Hope you had fun. My dad's taking us to the Taylor Swift concert, and we won't get home until late. Call you tomorrow!"

I was SHOCKED!! No wonder they tried so hard to get in touch with me . . . they were trying to include me in a SUPERcool, once-in-a-lifetime experience that Zoey's record-executive dad set up!!

I couldn't believe I missed it!!

I wrote back to the both of them: "OMG! I am so sorry. I really wish I was there with you guys!! Have fun!!"

Neither of them called me the next day, and their phones went right to voicemail when I tried to call them.

Then, to make matters worse, I got supersick on Sunday night and wasn't in school on Monday or today . . . and neither of them called to check on me!

I'm worried they're mad at me for ditching them. I mean, Brandon DID need my help, but still I feel superbad!

OMG, what if my two BFFs never speak to me again! ☹

WEDNESDAY

Today I was SUPERnervous going to school — what if Chloe and Zoey really were mad at me!

I went to their lockers before school and after my first class, but they weren't there! Then I saw them laughing

16

together at lunch, and I was just about to go over when MacKenzie walked by and said, "What's the matter, LOSER? Your friends don't want to sit with you?"

I was SO not in the mood for her nastiness!!

Then she said, "It was just a matter of time until they realized they're better off without you!"

So I said, "You must be mistaking them for Jessica, because SHE'S the one who'd be better off hanging out with a starving bear than YOU!" Only I said it in my head, so no one else heard it but me.

ORDINARILY, I would have thought MacKenzie was totally wrong, but I was feeling guilty about blowing Zoey and Chloe off, so I considered that maybe she was right.

I finally realized I was being silly and guessing at what they were thinking when really I needed to just ask!

I turned around to walk over to their lunch table, but they were gone.

By the time I got to my locker after lunch I was SO done with all the guessing! When I opened my locker, I found a note in there that read:

"Meet us in the janitor's closet ASAP!"

When I got there it was like I'd shrunk myself down and jumped into a piñata, because the room was FULL of streamers.

And not just streamers . . . Chloe was holding a Taylor Swift T-shirt and Zoey was holding up an autographed Taylor Swift poster.

They both yelled, "Surprise!"

Chloe said, "We missed you at the concert!! It would have been SO much cooler with you!"

And then Zoey said, "We tried to bring you this stuff on Monday, but your mom said it was best if we didn't bother you while you were sick!"

So that explains everything! They weren't mad at me . . . they were trying to be considerate!

I don't know why I went all drama queen over nothing. Chloe and Zoey are the best friends I've ever had. We're like Taylor Swift, Selena Gomez, and . . . well, a second Taylor Swift. That's how close we are!

They are definitely the BEST friends EVER!

WHAT KIND OF BFF ARE YOU?

I'm TOTALLY glad I'm not one of MacKenzie's mindless clones. Seriously, CCPs follow her around like the paparazzi follow Lindsay Lohan (except the CCPs probably aren't hoping to catch a wardrobe malfunction...). The other day I saw MacKenzie in the mall, totally trashing one of her "friends". Who does that?? Not you, I bet! You're probably an awesome friend. Not sure? Take the quiz and see!

1) You just had a HUGE fight with your BFF Jen, for the third time this week! As soon as you hang up the phone, you:

  a) Decide you are SO done with her. Then you invite all your other friends over and tell them that Jen is drama central and they should stay far, far away!

  b) Call your other BFF before Jen has a chance to do it. Then you try to get her to agree that Jen was totally wrong and owes you a BIG apology, ASAP!

  c) Cry—just a little! Then you call her back and try to smooth things over. It's your BFF you're talking about here!

2) You're in the janitor's closet at school chilling out (what, doesn't everyone do that?) when you overhear a bunch of girls making fun of your friend. You:

a) Might laugh if they say something funny. They're only joking. There's no reason to be all uptight about it!

b) Put on your iPod. It's not your job to be "mean police" but you don't have to listen to it, either!

c) Practically kick down the door and set those girls straight. No one disses your friends—end of story!

3) Your BFF broke her leg, so you promised her you'd watch movies with her instead of going to the school dance. Then your crush asks you to go! You know that:

a) Your friend will totally understand if you go to the dance. All good friends know that crushes come first!

b) This is one of the hardest decisions you'll have to make all week. Why does he have to be so cute?!?

c) He'll ask you to another dance some time, if he's really into you. So you tell him you already have a date with your bestie (even though it kind of hurts...)

4) Your friend's been hanging with some mean girls lately. (They make MacKenzie look as sweet as Selena Gomez . . . that's how nasty they are!) You:

  a) Just hang with your other friends. You're not going to beg her to spend time with you. If she forgot how awesome you are, then that's her loss!

  b) Wish you could do something about it. They might totally stab her in the back! But you don't think you can, so you just wait to see if she'll call you.

  c) Pull her aside and pinch her, because she must be under some kind of mean girl trance. There's no way you're letting them pull her to the dark side. She's way too good for that!

5) Your friend just said something really insensitive to you and it hurt your feelings. You think that:

  a) She totally meant to do it. You definitely don't trust her anymore, and you're going to tell her that!

  b) She was just having a bad day, but it was SO not cool! You'll definitely need a little while to cool off before you forgive her.

  c) She would never purposely hurt your feelings. So you ask her if there's something else bothering her. You're always there to help!

Mostly As:

Sometimes you put other people and things before your BFFs, and you don't always stick up for them. You also get angry with them kind of quickly. Next time, give them the benefit of the doubt. You don't want to end up without any true friends, like MacKenzie (OMG did I really just compare you to MacKenzie?!? Now I feel like a TOTALLY mean friend, because that was downright cruel!)

Mostly Bs:

OK, let me start by saying you're an awesome girl, but you're not always 100% loyal. You don't always defend your friends against mean girls, and you don't always try to fix things when you get into fights with them. Your BFFs love you, and they want to trust you, so don't forget to show them that they can, by being there for them!

Mostly Cs:

You're like Chloe and Zoey—a totally awesome friend! We'd definitely all hang out, because you never ditch your friends for guys, you always look out for them, and you're the first one to help when they go through rough times. If there was an Oscars ceremony for good friends, you'd be blubbering your way through an acceptance speech right now —that's what a great friend you are!

HOW TO PARTY LIKE A POP STAR!

Do you wish you could hang out with your friends all day AND all night? Me too! That's why I LOVE slumber parties! To keep things exciting, my sleepovers always have a theme. My fave is "Pop Star"! Now YOU can throw an all-night extravaganza just like mine!

The Preshow

INVITATIONS: You can make or buy your invitations, but just make sure they're glammed out with bling! Think glitter, gold, metallic paper, gemstones, or anything else that shines like a (pop) star.

DECORATIONS: Just go KA-RAY-ZEE! I used a hot-pink tablecloth with zebra-print paper plates and cups. Don't forget to sprinkle (fake) diamonds and colorful confetti everywhere.

MENU: Make a feast fit for a pop star with a fancy arrangement of finger foods! I served burger sliders, mini pizzas, hot dog wraps, and fruit dipped in chocolate.

CUPCAKE MICROPHONES: Dinner was delish, but the real showstopper was this fabulous dessert! To make your own, you'll need colorful ice-cream cones, cake mix, vanilla icing, and food coloring. With help from an adult, prepare your favorite cupcake mix and bake. Next tie a knot in one end of your red string licorice and insert your "cord" through a hole in the bottom of your "mic". You'll use colored icing as glue to stick a cupcake on top of a cone. Cover the entire cupcake

with icing, then add razzle-dazzle with silver sprinkles or sugar pearls!

The Main Event

After dinner, we attended the "Pyjammy Awards!" Chloe, Zoey and I took turns lip-synching our fave pop songs. We gave out awards for Best Performance,

Best Dance Moves, Best Dressed, and Best Pop Star Look-Alike. I can't believe I actually won a Pyjammy Award! Zoey got one too, but Chloe blew us away with her AMAZING impression of Katy Perry!!

Ask family members to be your audience. This will help you perform your best. Then WORK IT, GURRRL!!!!!

The Afterparty

Next we got cozy in our sleeping bags and watched our favorite musicals. Then we played games until we fell asleep. One of the games was called Dump, Date, or Marry. One of us named a Hollywood hunk, and we took turns sharing if we would dump, date, or marry him and why. To "date" means you think a boy is cute and fun. To "marry" means you're absolutely in LUVVV, and that hunk of a hunk is the best thing since smudge—free lip gloss! To "dump" is pretty obvious—you think a guy is too much drama or has the IQ of toilet paper!

SLEEPING MASKS: For a fun and creative activity, decorate sleeping masks. They make ADORKABLE party favors.

And always remember . . . What happens at the slumber party STAYS at the slumber party!

I hope your Pop Star slumber party is just as exciting as mine! And good luck at the Pyjammys! ☺!

??? QUESTION TIME! ???

It's time for more quick—fire questions!
Ready to dish about you and your besties??? GO!

Zoey and Chloe are my BFFs in the whole wide world.
Who are yours??

If you could be friends with a fictional character from a book
or TV show, who would it be?

What deep dark secret would you not tell anyone but your BFFs?

What's the most fun thing that you and your BFFs do together?

What do you think are the most important traits in a BFF?
How many of them do you think you fulfil?

Sometimes friendships change over time . . . do you have an
ex—friend that you wish you could make up with?

WHAT YOUR CRUSH SAYS ABOUT YOU!

Have you ever noticed how people look a lot like their dogs? It's totally true! My Paris-Hilton-with-a-perm neighbour could be her poodle's identical twin. I am SO not lying!

Anyway, I started thinking about how things you choose can say a lot about you. Random stuff like your favorite band, movie or even make-up brand can be a reflection of YOU! Which means that REALLY important things like who your friends are and . . . hmmmm . . . how about . . . what type of guy you crush on, can really say a lot about you as a person!

YEP! That's right, the guy who gives you a severe case of ROLLER COASTER SYNDROME says something about you!

Interested? Well read on to see what your type of guy says about you . . .

IF YOU LIKE EMO GUYS (Think Edward from *Twilight*)

You're the kind of girl who likes to talk about things . . . A LOT! You crush on emo boys because they're all sensitive and stuff. Just beware the moody ones. Sometimes dark and brooding guys can be kind of a downer!

IF YOU LIKE TROUBLE MAKERS (You know, the boy who spends all his time in the principal's office)

You don't really like following the rules and you crush on boys who make their own. Let's face it: there's something kind of exciting about a boy who's totally unpredictable. It's like, what will that crazy kid do next?! A word of caution, my rebel—loving friends: sometimes the bad boy is BAD news!!

IF YOU LIKE PREPPY GUYS (Think collared shirts and feel of being ironed from head to toe)

You're totally organized, and probably have color—coordinated folders for every subject. A preppy boy makes you weak in the khaki knees!!

IF YOU LIKE MUSICIAN TYPES (This one is fairly obvious, but I'm talking about members of the next One-D)

You're totally into music, and you're probably also super creative, just like your crush. And let's be honest: you also like attention. Everyone's always like, "Nice set for the talent show!" or "Saw you on YouTube!" or "Would you sign my forehead?!?"

IF YOU LIKE SPORTY GUYS (Football, baseball, basketball, any-kind-of-ball)

You very well may be reading this with pom poms mere meters away. Cheerleaders are ALL ABOUT sporty guys! They're not the only ones, though. Girls who crush on jocks usually fall into two categories: CCP or aspiring-to-be-CCP.

IF YOU LIKE GEEKY GUYS (Boys that know more about the relativity theory than the latest teen movie)

You're a huge fan of *The Big Bang Theory* and dream of finding your own Leonard or even maybe a Sheldon! You're also probably just waiting for the right guy to whisk you off to Comic Con so you can show off your home-made cosplay!

IF YOU LIKE ART-SHOW BOYS (Boys who always seem to have a pencil behind their ear or paint on their clothes)

You're probably massively creative and kind of cool and quiet. You and your crush could spend hours just hanging out at your local art supplies store or wandering round galleries looking for inspiration.

So . . . what type of crush-itis are you suffering from: Emo, Bad Boy, Preppy, Pop Star, Sporty, Geek or Art-show guy?

IS HE INTO YOU TOO?

So, you know that you like him, but how do you know if the feeling is mutual? There's nothing more annoying than having a big fat crush on someone and not knowing if he likes you!

Doesn't it drive you crazy when he smiles at you in the hallway, and you're not sure if it's because he thinks you look super cute OR he's really smiling at the CCP behind you? Or what about when he asks for your phone number, and you're not sure if it's because he can't wait to talk to you after school OR he wants to have it in case he needs help with his homework some time?

Totally stressful right? Why don't boys just come right out and say, "I think you're awesome and I have a big fat crush on you!!"?

So, since we're all way too scared to just tell each other what's up, I came up with the little guide based on super scientific research (by "super scientific research," I've watched a LOT of those advice shows on TV).

You know your crush is DEFINITELY into you when:

1) You catch him looking at you in class. Did you just happen to lock eyes five times while taking a test recently? Unless you had the answers written on the side of your face, it's because he's TOTALLY INTO YOU!

2) He pauses a lot when he's talking to you. It's probably not because he's a superslow thinker. It's because he wants to say the right things because he's TOTALLY INTO YOU!

3) He drops things a lot when he talks to you. It's not because he has some kind of weird tremor. He's just nervous because he's TOTALLY INTO YOU!

4) He asks your friends stuff about you. I know, I know, he could be completing an English

assignment to write about all the girls in school. OR maybe it's the way more obvious answer . . . He's TOTALLY INTO YOU!

5) He laughs at your jokes, even the silly ones. That knock-knock joke you busted out in homeroom? Nope, not funny! It's just that he's TOTALLY INTO YOU!

6) He defends you against CCPs. Remember when that evil girl said something obnoxious, like, "Where did you buy your shirt? The 99 Cents Store??" And he was all like, "I think it's kind of cool." He's not just REALLY into girls' fashion. It's just that he's TOTALLY INTO YOU!

So that's my SUPERscientific research! What do you think . . . good stuff? If your crush likes you too, how did you find out?

THE BIOLOGY OF MY HEARTBREAK
By Nikki Maxwell

I see you in my dreams
in your favorite white
button-down shirt,
sitting across from me
in the cafeteria.
I've never seen anyone
eat fries so beautifully.

I see you in biology class,
taking pictures for
the school newspaper, when
you whisper to the depths of my soul,
"Hold the frog at an angle."

For it is only you
who can make a photo
of a dissected frog
seem so vibrant.
So alive. Yet dead.

It hurts to feel this way,
to know that you'll never know me.
To want to run my fingers
through your dark, wavy hair,
as I realize that
the putrid smell of formaldehyde
and the dull gaze of a lifeless frog
will forever remind ME of US!

WEDNESDAY

OMG!! BIG NEWS!!! Brandon came over to my house to work on a biology project last night!

That morning, I was SO excited!! I knew we'd have a good two hours to talk about all kinds of fun things . . . like DNA, molecules, and osmosis.

Just kidding! I'm not such a massive dork that I CAN'T WAIT to discuss the inner workings of the human body in my free time!

That's the stuff we were SUPPOSED to talk about, but I planned to discuss way cooler things . . . like fun stuff we could do together during Easter break!

I had it all planned out in my head: we'd order pizza, take it up to my room, and put the "No Brianna" sign on my door. (The one with her head in a circle and a diagonal line going through it!)

Then we'd spend about 15 minutes working on our project before spending the rest of the night giggling, flirting, and, okay, who I am kidding . . . probably blushing, staring at our feet, and being completely awkward!

Still, awkward blushing with Brandon is better than most things with everyone else!

The fantasy was pretty short-lived, though, because my mom had to go and ruin everything with seven horrible words: "We'd love to have Brandon for dinner!"

First of all, that would take AT LEAST a half hour, and I could think of a million and one better ways to waste our time, like folding my dad's underwear together or singing "This is the Song That Never Ends" for thirty minutes straight. (Yup, I thought it would be that bad!)

But more importantly, I just knew that if my mom had a chance to talk to Brandon, she'd not only ask him a ton of stuff that's none of her business, she'd also do something to humiliate me, like pull out pictures of me as a baby, naked in the sink.

So, when the doorbell rang, I jumped down the stairs so fast that I tripped and ended up banging into the door.

And THAT'S how I greeted Brandon . . . with a big, loud thud, followed by an awkward "Hi" as I rubbed my aching shoulder. Still, I forgot all about the pain once I saw his cute face!

Within minutes, we were sitting at the kitchen table, where my mom was pretty much staring at him with this super weird look on her face. Every now and then, when he wasn't looking, she'd try to get my attention and then mouth something creepy about him, like, "He's cute!" So gross!

After that, my dad bored us with a super long rant about bugs.

Brandon is cute!

Though in his defense, Brandon had said, "Sure, Mr. Maxwell. I'd love to hear about the latest advancements in pest control." (He's SUCH a sweet liar!)

Once my dad finished, Brandon told another whopper, saying, "Gee, Mrs. Maxwell, this is the best meatloaf I've ever tasted."

My mom responded, "I'm glad you're enjoying it! You know, there's something I'd like to show you." Then she got up and started moving toward her hope chest, where I know she keeps all her photo albums.

OMG, I was TERRIFIED! I just knew she was going to pull out my baby pictures, and I definitely didn't want that! The next bit felt like it happened in slow motion. I saw her. I panicked. I lunged. I shouted, "Nooooooo!"

And then I practically slammed the chest shut. Everyone was just staring at me, like I was some kind of crazy woman!

My mom said, "Wow, Nikki, I didn't know you were so protective of Grandma's meatloaf recipe."

My face turned BRIGHT RED, and I said something totally dumb, like, "Oh, well, it's, like, a Maxwell family secret!

I thought for sure Brandon was going to think I was some kind of lunatic after that. But when we got to my room 15 minutes later, he said, "I've had a really great time, Nikki. I really hope we can hang out again soon!"

Squeeee!! Brandon wants to hang out! I may have bruised my shoulder and embarrassed myself big time, but it was the best night ever! ☺

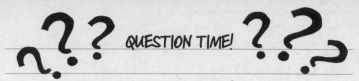

QUESTION TIME!

Ready?? Here are some quick-fire questions
about boys and crushes . . . remember to be honest with your
answers—dorks don't judge each other!

Who would you LOVE to get a Valentine's gift from?

What do you think is the best way of showing
your crush you like them?

Have you ever done something crazy to impress a crush?

If you could design your own love hearts, what would they say?

Who is the celeb that you have the biggest crush on?

Smart, cute, or funny? What characteristic makes
you crush on someone?

FAMILY
DRAMA-RAMAS

MY CRAZY FAMILY

Everyone thinks they have a crazy family, but mine seems to be the craziest of them all! Brianna's best friend is an old lady she makes out of her hand, my dad is a HUGE klutz who rides around in a van with a giant bug on its roof and then my mom is just busy trying crazy-hard to keep us all in check! The other thing about my mom is that she likes us to have "family fun days", which nearly always turn out to be disasters! But sunshine or rain, snow or hail, we're out there having "fun" together . . .

OUR FAMILY BARBECUE PICNIC (A STORY IN PICTURES)

THE END

FAMILY ROAD TRIP ESSENTIALS

Yipppppeeeee!! Even though being around my family can be super stressful, I LOVE going on holiday with them especially when we go to cool places where there's a TON of fun stuff to do like bike riding, renting a boat, and campfire cook-outs. OMG so fun!!

The only problem is, going on family holidays usually means family road trips which are disasters waiting to happen! Even just a few hours in the car means there's a distinct possibility I may die from Briannitis (the clinical name for Brianna overexposure).

Since spending time in an enclosed space with my whole family feels a lot like getting a root canal, I've come up with a list of road trip essentials. This way, I'll have tons of stuff to keep myself busy, so I can tune out my family.

- ★ iPod, loaded with every song by Justin Bieber, Katy Perry, Rihanna, Selena Gomez, and Lady Gaga
- ★ My sketchbook, colored pencils, colored pens, and assorted markers
- ★ At least four magazines
- ★ One, preferably two, puzzle books
- ★ My diary (OMG can you imagine the panic if I left that behind!)
- ★ A portable DVD player
- ★ A super-soft pillow, in case I feel like dreaming of all the fun I'm going to have over the holiday!
- ★ A bag of snacks, including crackers, cookies, cupcakes, chips, pretzels, and an apple (to put on top, so my Mom assumes it's a bunch of healthy stuff)
- ★ A camera to take tons of pictures that I will later complain I can't add to Facebook, since Mom is totally weird about me putting personal pictures online
- ★ Masking tape, to tape a line on the middle of the back seat that Brianna is absolutely NOT allowed to cross!

That's what I need to survive, but what about you? Any top tips?

SUNDAY

Have you ever yelled, "Moooooom!" and then because she didn't answer you yelled it again, and again, and again, and again, until finally she screamed from another room, "Whaaaaat?!?"

Maybe you were in the bathroom and you needed a little toilet paper 'cause the roll was out. Or maybe you had to ask her a SUPERpressing question, like whether she'd drive you to the mall in an hour. So you just kinda started screaming for her, knowing she'd eventually hear if you yelled a little louder every time.

Brianna has been doing that to me for the last fifteen minutes and I refuse to give in and answer!! I'm SO not her mom, and it won't work on me!

I know it may sound kind of mean. You might be thinking, "What if she fell and broke her leg?!?"

Well, first let me remind you this isn't my 90-year-old great-grandmother I'm talking about. Brianna drinks a ton of milk and her bones are just fine! And let me further remind you I know Brianna's I'm-in-serious-trouble-and-really-need-help scream. This isn't it! This is her I'm-lazy-and-I-want-something-from-you scream, and it

won't work on me! Sorry, thanks for playing, game over!
  So just to keep myself busy until she gets tired and
gives up . . . or screams one too many times and loses her
voice . . . I've decided to list the top 7 most annoying
things about my bratty sister.

1) Brianna jumps on my bed at 7:00 every Saturday
   morning, singing, "Five little monkeys jumping on
   the bed!" Yup, that's what I wake up to at a
   RIDICULOUSLY early hour. I know . . . crazy, huh?

2) Whenever she eats mashed potatoes, she puts her nose
   in her plate pretending to be a little piggy eating out
   of a trough.

3) She screams almost everything that she says while
   we're hanging out in the backyard because, as she
   says, "I DON'T GOTS TO USE MY INDOOR VOICE
   BECAUSE WE'RE NOT INSIDE!!!!!"

4) She asks a question, and then after I answer, asks,
   "Why?" And then after I answer THAT, she asks,
   "Why?" And then when I answer THAT. . . It just
   goes on and on and on! And it's unbearable!!

5) The second I get on the phone, she sits next to me
   and starts poking at my side to get my attention.
   Why in the world she waits until then, I have no idea!

6) Oh, oh Miss Penelope! I can't believe I got this far

in the list before mentioning Miss Penelope! Only a
totally warped little human would turn her hand into
a tiny decapitated person. So WEIRD!!

7) She's STILL calling my name!! Okay, that's it. Little
sister is going down!!! BRB . . .

Awwwww! Okay, so I totally have the sweetest little sister
in the whole wide world. I stormed into her room all annoyed
and ready to scream, and guess what I saw? You'll never
guess! You guessing?

Brianna decorated her whole room with streamers and
hung up this picture she drew of the two of us holding
hands. Then when I walked in, she said, "Surprise! Thanks
for being an awesome sister!"

Then she asked me to sit down for a tea party with her,
which I usually find super lame, but she had Mom make my
favorite red velvet cake!

I asked, "What's all this for??" And then she goes, "Can't
a girl just love her sister?"

I take it back. Brianna is
not annoying OR a brat . . .
well, not always! I love that
little weirdo!

MAXWELL FAMILY ALBUM

Even though my family can be a total nightmare and OMG sooooo embarrassing, I still wouldn't swap them for the world!

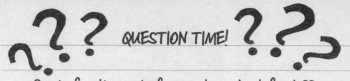

QUESTION TIME!

Ready for the quick-fire questions about family??
Okay, three, two, one . . . GO!

What thing does your mom or dad say over and over
(and over!) again like a broken record?

What's the nicest thing you've done for someone in your
family recently? What's the nicest thing one of them
have done for YOU?

If you could give away one thing that your parents
own to charity, what would it be and why?

What's your idea of a dream family fun day out?

What famous TV family is most like yours? How are you similar?

Who is the kookiest member of your family?

SCHOOL'S OUT!

WHAT DOES YOUR FAVOURITE SUBJECT SAY ABOUT YOU?

MATHS

You're practical, logical and like solving problems, which means you're a great friend to have around in a crisis because you like to think things through. Just remember to trade that number 2 pencil for a paintbrush or hairbrush–microphone sometimes, because being creative can be a blast too!

ENGLISH

You love reading and stories and you're always dreaming up ideas for your next novel! Just don't forget that real life can be as fun as fiction, so sometimes you need to close the book and open up to what's going on around you. Don't worry, you can still be a published author someday, even if you let loose and be a kid now!

READING... AN EXTREME SPORT!

ART

Just like me you totally love to doodle and let your creative juices flow! And maybe you're also known as the go-to girl for fake tattoos. There just may be a museum exhibit in your future...but only if you pay attention in your other classes, too. Behind every successful artist there are years of a totally boring but super useful education!

SCIENCE

Experiments and theories are your favorite things and you dream of being a rocket scientist! If your friends are science nuts too, then you've probably got great "chemistry"(!), just be careful around flammable substances . . . school science labs are expensive to replace!

HISTORY

You love all things historical and kind of wish you were born a Victorian lady (if Victorian ladies had iPhones and hairdryers!). You think it's totally cool to read about how people used to live, and this makes you a really open-minded friend. Keep learning about and from the past and you'll have an AWESOME future!

GEOGRAPHY

Nothing gets you more excited than a spinning globe because you can't wait to explore this big, awesome planet! Just remember to look before you leap. I know, the world isn't flat, so it's not like you'll fall off or anything . . . but sometimes adventurers like you need a reminder to slow down and enjoy the journey!

GYM CLASS

You're like a Jack-in-the-Box, DYING to bust out and impossible to hold down! Running, jumping, tennis, football, netball, swimming, cycling . . . if it's active, you're in! Sports can be a

blast, so long as you don't get too competitive. I know, it sounds like your mom would say (Sorry!) but having fun is WAY more important
than winning!

COMPUTER SCIENCE

You're a total techy who always has to have the latest gadgets and gizmos, and you're online 24/7 because you never want to miss out. You just may invent the new Facebook someday, but in the meantime, remember that your smartphone isn't actually part of your hand . . . and there's a lot of life you CAN'T experience on a tiny screen!

THE STUDENT HANDBOOK OF HOMEWORK EXCUSES FOR LAZY DUMMIES

I can't believe how much homework they give you in middle school. There's just NO WAY you can get all of it done.

One time when I had LOADS of homework, I decided to come up with a really good excuse so my teacher would give me extra time to finish my assignment.

For some reason, teachers tend to believe stories that are really supercreative, no matter how crazy or far-fetched. So I tried to think of something really good and that's when I came up with the brilliant idea for a handy-dandy manual.

I decided to write down all the best excuses I've used over the years and place them in a simple form. And, once I've collected enough of them, I can publish them as a book that could possibly become an overnight bestseller for students around the world!

What do YOU think? Awesome idea, right?

FROM: _____
(YOUR NAME)

RE: Issue with My School Assignment

Dear_____,
(NAME OF TEACHER)

You probably won't believe this, but
☐ my spoiled sister
☐ my bratty brother
☐ my paranoid uncle
☐ my senile neighbour lady

has a pet
☐ snake, named Hubert,
☐ monkey, named Rocky,
☐ vampire bat, named Jean-Claude,
☐ unicorn, named Buttercup,

that unfortunately got really

- ☐ frightened
- ☐ angry
- ☐ confused
- ☐ sick

and unexpectedly

- ☐ projectile vomited on
- ☐ had babies on
- ☐ had a heart attack and died on
- ☐ had a really bad nosebleed on

my

- ☐ math problems.
- ☐ assignment.
- ☐ project.
- ☐ report.
- ☐ homework.
- ☐ _____.
  (FILL IN THE BLANK)

When I realized I would not be turning this in to you on time, I became gravely depressed and suffered uncontrollable

- ☐ sobbing.
- ☐ flatulence.
- ☐ hiccups.
- ☐ laughter.

I am truly very sorry for any inconvenience this may have caused.

I assure you, it will *NOT* happen again

- ☐ *EVER!*
- ☐ until my next homework assignment is due.
- ☐ until the cow jumps over the moon.
- ☐ until the next exciting episode of *America's Next Top Model.*
- ☐ (and if you believe this, I'd like to sell you some ~~swamp~~ land in Florida).

Sincerely, _____
                    (YOUR SIGNATURE)

WEDNESDAY

I. Am. Freaking. OUT!!!

You know how Brandon's my biology partner? Well, I've been spending A LOT of time writing notes to him in class.

At the beginning of class today, my teacher saw me passing him a note, so she said, "Miss Maxwell! Unless that's about today's material, I suggest you put it away RIGHT NOW!"

After that I had an idea . . . write notes in code so it WAS related to the schoolwork!

So I wrote a note that read:

Cell membranes are really, unbelievably interesting! It's way fun to study this stuff! And I can't stop thinking about genotypes! But what I really love are unicellular organisms... For real, this biology class is awesome. And our **teacher** is clever and highly knowledgeable. Education is cool!

So when you put the bold letters together, there was a secret message that read: "Maybe want to hang after school?"

I figured this way, if my teacher grabbed the note, she'd be SUPERflattered and say, "Sorry, Miss Maxwell. I was wrong to doubt your focus and scholarly aptitude. Carry on!"

But instead, she saw me from the front of the class

and said, "Miss Maxwell, are you still passing notes? Stand up and read that for the entire class!"

I SO didn't see that coming . . . and I don't know why! It happens in ALL the school movies!!

I REALLY didn't want to read what I wrote since it was just, well, weird! But I couldn't think of anything else on the spot. Also, I was afraid I'd get in even more trouble if I didn't read the actual note and then she found out!

So I stood in front of the WHOLE CLASS and stuttered: "Cell membranes are, um, really, unbelievably interesting. It's, um . . . it's way fun to study this stuff. And I can't stop thinking about genotypes. But what I really love are unicellular organisms."

At that point EVERYONE was laughing at me, and I was sweating so much it looked like I had two soaked sponges wedged under my armpits!

My teacher thought I was making this up, so she said, "Is that really ALL you wrote? What else is on that note, Miss Maxwell?"

And then I finished with, "For real, this biology class is . . . um . . . awesome. And our teacher is clever and highly knowledgeable. Education is cool!"

I thought I was going to HURL!

Brandon was looking at me with this confused look on his face. He didn't know there was a code in it!

Then my teacher said, "If that's REALLY what you wrote, I severely misjudged you, and for that I am sorry."

I breathed a big sigh of relief after that! I looked like a TOTAL science nerd, but at least I could stop worrying about her hating me!

Right when I was walking out of class, she grabbed my arm and said, "You're right, education IS cool! Tomorrow you're going to be my special assistant in teaching the lesson. It will be 'awesome'!"

So now I have to spend the whole next class being her "special assistant" . . . in front of everyone!

THURSDAY

I didn't even tell you the worst part about what happened after class yesterday!

After I tossed the note in the trashcan, I ran out the door to follow Brandon so I could explain what had really happened.

I mean, there are worse things in the world than your crush thinking you're SO into biology that you write long, geeky notes about it, but still, I wanted to give him the REAL message!

Once I caught up with him, he jokingly said, "Now I know what to get you for your birthday . . . biology flash cards, because education is cool!"

I got SO RED that my face looked like a huge glob of ketchup with eyes! Right as I was about to explain the coded message about hanging out after school, he said, "Got to run . . . I've got a doctor's appointment. See you later!"

I was disappointed because I was REALLY looking forward to spending more time with him, but also, I was hoping he'd help me come up with an excuse to avoid playing teacher's assistant.

I asked Chloe and Zoey for advice, but neither was all that helpful.

Chloe said, "You should do it! It could be an AWESOME opportunity to impress Brandon!"

Apparently, she forgot Brandon ISN'T Bill Nye the Science Guy and is in NO WAY impressed by a passion for biology!

Zoey said, "You should just tell your teacher the truth. 'Honesty is the first chapter in the book of wisdom.' Thomas Jefferson."

Another suggestion I filed under, "Well-meaning but totally unhelpful advice from friends!"

Since I had to go to school, and biology was my first class, I had to come up with something at the last minute. I was FREAKING OUT!

Right after I sat down, I took out my notebook and started jotting something down super fast.

Brandon looked at me with this totally cute smirk and whispered, "Writing a note, huh? Haven't you learned anything?"

He was SO flirting with me!

Right then my teacher walked in and said, "Good morning, class! I'm excited to have Miss Maxwell helping me out today!"

I stumbled to the front of the room and handed her the note I'd written. It said: "I REALLY wanted to help with the lesson today . . . but I have laryngitis!"

She read it and then said, "That's okay . . . you won't need your voice!"

Then she pulled out this weird looking one-piece costume that looked like a human body with no skin, and said, "Today we're going to review the human anatomy . . . all you need to do is put this on over your clothes. I'll point things out and do all the talking!

OMG, I was HORRIFIED! I REALLY didn't want to stand in front of the whole class wearing it, but I had to stand with my arms and legs out for almost twenty minutes, and it was INSANELY awkward and embarrassing!!

After she told me I could take the costume off and go to my desk, I handed it to her and she whispered, "Maybe want to hang after school?"

I thought that was TOTALLY inappropriate and weird,

since she's in her forties and doesn't seem like the hang-around-talking-about-crushes type.

Then I remembered . . . the code! She must have grabbed the note and figured the whole thing out. And the human anatomy costume thing was payback!

After class, I explained the whole thing to Brandon, and told him . . . I have DEFINITELY learned my lesson. No more passing notes for me . . . it's not worth the HUMILIATION!

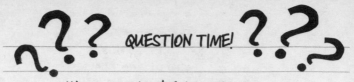

QUESTION TIME!

It's pop quiz time! Get your brain in gear,
your pencils sharpened and make sure not to copy
anyone else's answers . . .

What's your hardest subject at school? What's your easiest?

You've totally blinged out your locker at school,
what does it look like?

Who should win Coolest Teacher award at your school and why?

What do you hope will happen by the end of this school year?

What girl at your school most reminds you of MacKenzie?

If you were your school principal what would you do
to make your school more fun?

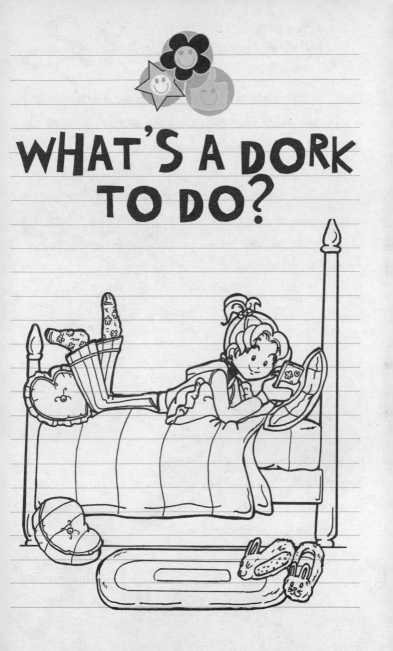

Okay, firstly, I am NOT a fashionista like MacKenzie or any of the other CCP girls! But I always try to rock the dork-chic look as much as I can!

MacKenzie and her friends might be all:

"HI, SWEETIE! YOU'RE UNDER ARREST FOR A FELONY FASHION VIOLATION!"

And even though that means I kind of feel like doing this:

GASOLINE

I know that I shouldn't listen to anyone and, dress how I want to.

It's my style and no one else's!

What I really HATE are clothes that are "SNOBBY CHIC". That's when the exact same outfit looks TOTALLY different on two very similar girls. The more popular you are at school, the BETTER it looks on you, and the more unpopular you are, the WORSE it looks on you. I can't tell you HOW a snobby chic outfit mysteriously knows all of this personal stuff about you, but it obviously DOES!

WHY I HATE SNOBBY CHIC FASHIONS!

↑
COOL SNOBBY
CHIC OUTFIT AT
THE MALL!

↑
POPULAR
GIRL

UNPOPULAR
GIRL ←

The SNOBBY CHIC phenomenon is quite a mind-boggling thing. Hopefully, Congress will allocate funding for scientists to study it, along with how socks mysteriously disappear from the dryer. But, until then, BUYER BEWARE ☺!

Just for fun, here are some fashion looks I tried out while shopping with my mom and Brianna! What do you think?? Are any of them totally me? Or maybe one of these looks is just like your dorky style?

WACKO EMO

DRAMA QUEEN MEAN

RAGING REBEL ROCKER

COS GIRL CUTIE →

SILLY CELEBUTANT

← BAGGY SHABBY CHIC

Personally, I love wearing anything that makes me feel comfortable and happy, but sometimes it's nice to get dressed up like a princess too! I wore this outfit to the school dance I went to with Brandon (squeee!), and it's totally one of my favorite dresses!

PLAY THAT FUNKY MUSIC

I LOVE being in a band with all of my friends, especially since that includes Brandon! (Squeee!) I have such a blast hanging out with them, making cool music together. Even if we totally stunk at singing and playing instruments, I'd be all about our band. It's SO much fun! Okay, I'm not going to lie. It was pretty sweet to win the school talent show! (Music + friends + prize money = a whole lot of snoopy happy dancing!) But you don't need to sign up for a talent show to start jamming with your friends. Not sure what to sing? Try our winning song!

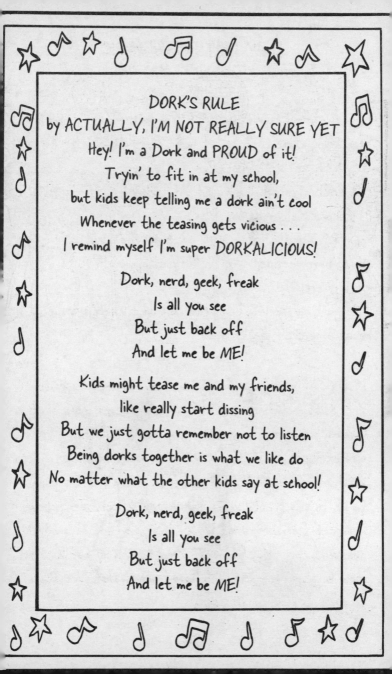

LET'S GET PHYSICAL
– EXERCISE THE NIKKI MAXWELL WAY

My health and fitness are VERY important to me. So I've been doing these exercises at home every day to try to stay in shape.

Unfortunately, I just found out today I was doing ALL of them totally WRONG ☺!!

I'm SO disgusted! This is all my teacher's fault. She should have provided specific instructions on HOW to DO these exercises.

So, just on case you're as clueless about exercise as me, here's a handy guide . . .

EXERCISE #1: CURL-UPS

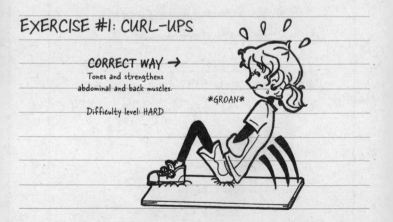

CORRECT WAY →
Tones and strengthens
abdominal and back muscles.

Difficulty level: HARD

GROAN

← INCORRECT WAY

My CURL-UPS make my
hair curly and bouncy.
They are easy to do with
exercise equipment like a
curling iron. After fifteen
minutes of these, you'll look
superCUTE!

Difficulty level: EASY

EXERCISE #2: PUSH-UPS

← CORRECT WAY

Strengthens shoulder, arm,
abdominal and leg muscles.

Difficulty level: VERY HARD

GRUNT

INCORRECT WAY →

My PUSH-UP ice-cream cup is
good exercise for my tongue,
lips and chin. The best part is
that it tastes really yummy.

Difficulty level: VERY EASY

EXERCISE #3: PULL-UPS

UGH

CORRECT WAY →
Strengthens and tones arm
and back muscles.

Difficulty level:
NEXT TO IMPOSSIBLE

← INCORRECT WAY
My PULL-UPS are great
for socks, pants, tights, gym
shorts and anything else that
has a tendency to fall down
around your ankles. It exercises
fingers and improves balance.

Difficulty level: EASY

EXERCISE #4: CRUNCHES

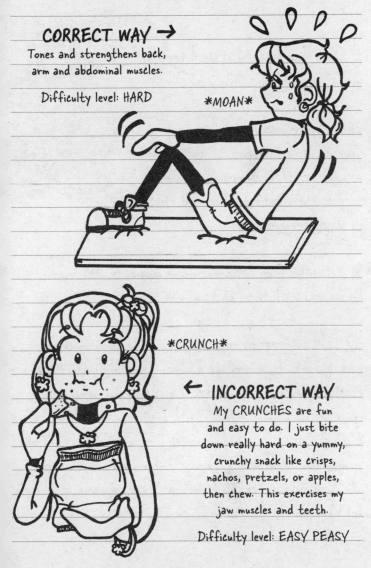

CORRECT WAY →

Tones and strengthens back, arm and abdominal muscles.

Difficulty level: HARD

MOAN

CRUNCH

← INCORRECT WAY

My CRUNCHES are fun and easy to do. I just bite down really hard on a yummy, crunchy snack like crisps, nachos, pretzels, or apples, then chew. This exercises my jaw muscles and teeth.

Difficulty level: EASY PEASY

5 THINGS TO DO WHEN YOU'RE BORED

1) Make your bratty little sister give you a manicure and pedicure.

2) Use your mad art skills to give yourself a pen tattoo . . . but don't let anyone see it! They might all want you to give them tattoos, too, and that can be superoverwhelming!

3) Recreate your favourite movie moments with your BFFs and post them on YouTube!

4) Take pictures of your old clothes so you can show your parents that you are fashion-challenged and they absolutely HAVE to take you for a shopping spree.

5) Pretend you're living in a real-life social network. Poke your siblings. Give your parents status updates: "I just ate a rice krispie treat. Yum!" or "I have to pee so bad! TTYL!"

IF YOU CAN'T STAND THE HEAT,
GET OUT OF THE KITCHEN!

Cooking can be a super fun thing to do with your family and friends (especially since you have something yummy to eat when you're done!). But it's probably way more fun with friends if, like me, you have a bratty little sister who loves to paint the walls with ketchup and then cry, "Nikki did it!" knowing your parents just MIGHT believe it because you're into art!

I've had A TON of disasters cooking with Brianna. This one time she and I tried to cook a gourmet dinner for my parents including frogs' legs(!) and she made me put all the frogs back in the pond before we even really got started! Then, another time I promised my mom I'd bake the Christmas cookies with Brianna and this happened . . .

I told Miss Penelope NOT to turn the oven on high. But she wanted the cookies to get done fast 'cause she's really HUNGRY!

84

opened the windows to clear out all the smoke and hoped the fire department wouldn't show up. OMG! I'll just DIE if my face ends up plastered on the front page of the city newspaper!

ME, PLASTERED ACROSS THE FRONT PAGE

o that little baking project was a complete and utter ISASTER!

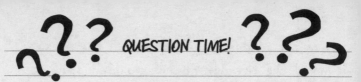

QUESTION TIME!

I hope you're ready to answer my questions about all the dorkalicious things that you like to do in your spare time!

WOW! You have a video on YouTube with one million views! What are you doing in it?

What was the last film you saw that scared you so badly you had to sleep with the lights on?

If you could perform in the school talent show, what would you do?

If you're dressing to impress, what outfit would you wear?

I'm totally obsessed by ART — what activity are you totally obsessed with?

Do you have a secret recipe that no one else knows how to make? What is it?

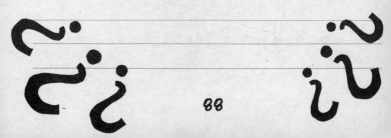

HOW TO WRITE YOUR OWN DORK DIARY!

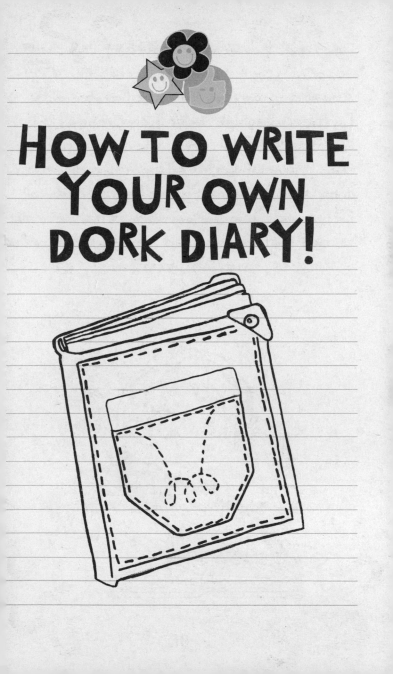

Sometimes it feels like writing in my diary is what keeps me sane when the rest of my life is totally KRA-AZY! Being able to rant about MacKenzie, remember the fun times I've had with Chloe and Zoey, relive my RCS moments with Brandon or even write down the weird things Brianna has done in my diary means that I get the drama out of my head and stop it from EXPLODING!! Everyone should have their own diary and it's, like, so easy to start! Want to write a diary like mine? Here are a few of my top tips for getting started . . .

← ME, FEELING BETTER AFTER VENTING IN MY DIARY!

Tip One: DISCOVER YOUR DIARY IDENTITY

Answer the following questions to find out the best type of diary for you.

1) It's Saturday afternoon. Your homework is all done and you have an hour to do whatever you want. You decide to:

a) Play an exciting round of your favorite computer or video game.

b) Spend time relaxing by reading that new book your BFF has been raving about.

c) Check in with your friends via email, text or a social networking site like Everloop.

d) Let your creative juices flow by darwing your favorite anime characters.

2) You left your diary in your third-hour English class, and your secret crush returns it to you during lunch. You:

a) Email him one of those cute animated thank-you e-cards and surprise him with his fave chocolate bar as a reward!

b) Gag on your meat loaf and then rush to the girls' bathroom, where you spend the rest of the day hiding out in a locked stall.

c) Hope he read the part in your diary about you liking him, so he'll *finally* ask you to the school dance. Hey, it's only a week away!

d) Blush profusely when he compliments that funky self-portrait in glitter you're working on for the art show, and offer to draw a zany caricature of him as a thank-you.

3) When something is really bothering you, you usually:

a) Ponder the problem for an hour or two and then try to forget about it by doing a self-induced brain freeze with three gallons of Ben & Jerry's Chunky Monkey ice cream.

b) Privately obsess over the problem all day long while trying to convince everyone who asks "Are you okay?" that you're fine and nothing is bothering you because (1) your problem is way too complicated for them to understand, and (2) you're way too exhausted from pretending you're just fine to explain it to them.

c) Vent about the problem rather loudly to anyone and everyone who'll listen to you. Because if YOU ain't happy, NOBODY should be happy!

d) Distract yourself from worrying by channeling all that negative energy into a creative project. Like painting a still-life mural inside your locker and adding a water fountain, scented candles, and a yoga mat, and then totally chilling out in between classes.

4) Your birthday was three months ago and you still need to send your grandma a think-you note for that hideous avocado-green sweater she knitted for you that was two sizes too big and more itchy than a severe case of poison ivy. You:

a) Drop her a quick e-mail sincerely telling her how you'll cherish her gift forever, while casually mentioning how much you really, really LOVE gift cards because one size fits all and they don't usually cause a rash.

94

b) Compose a heartfelt, handwritten thank-you note informing her that her gift is being worn almost daily. But you leave out the part about how you buried it out in the backyard and your dad accidentally found it when he was watering the grass and now it's his lucky bowling sweater.

c) Friend your grandma online and then post your thank-you note on her page along with a picture of yourself in the sweater SHE knitted so that her fourteen online friends can see it. But you also wear the ski mask YOU knitted so that your 1,784 online friends won't recognize you in a sweater that looks like dirty yak fur.

d) Paint a life-size portrait of yourself wearing the sweater and send it to your grandma to show your gratitude. Because thanks to her, some very lucky dog or cat at the local animal shelter will give birth to her litter on a warm, fuzzy, two-sizes-too-big avocado-green sweater.

5) Which of the following is most true?

a) You're a very tech-savvy person.
You're a team player and always up for a
challenge.

b) You're friendly and a hopeless romantic.
You love curling up in a comfy blanket and
daydreaming.

c) You're happy and have lots of friends.
There's always some type of drama going on
in your life.

d) You're creative and enjoy art, music, drama,
   and poetry. Your personal style is unique and
   slightly edgy.

6) **You hear the news that your BFF's soccer team just
won the regional championship. You:**

a) Send her the text message "YOU GO, GIRL!
   Congrats!"

b) Congratulate her with a big hug when you
   see her.

c) Leave her a phone message of you screaming
   hysterically.

d) Surprise her with a hand-made poster on her
   locker that says "Congrats! You ROCK!"

7) You're about to wash your favorite pair of jeans and find ten dollars stashed in the back pocket from your last babysitting job. You're RICH! So you treat yourself to:

a) A ticket to that blockbuster movie based on your favorite book. You've been waiting, like, FOREVER for it to come out!

b) Gourmet CUPCAKES! SQUEEEEEE!!

c) Lip gloss! There's a buy-two-get-one-free
sale at the mall!

d) Music for your iPod. There are some new tunes
you've heard lately that are real ear candy.

2) You're at a slumber party and it's game time. Which
of the following would you rather play?

a) Just Dance

b) The Game of Life

c) Truth or Dare

d) Pictionary

Now look back at which answer you circled for each
question.

Which letter do you have the most of?

I have mostly _____.

Mostly As:

You are smart and curious, and you like learning new things. You will most enjoy keeping a diary on your computer. Write detailed entries about your interesting adventures and new discoveries.

Mostly Bs:

You are kind and sensitive, and you like helping others. You will most enjoy writing in a diary or journal. Your dreams and feelings are sacred. Share them with your diary like a best friend.

Mostly Cs:

You are friendly and outgoing, and you love people. You will most enjoy writing a blog. Select a fab online ID and share your exciting, DIVALICIOUS life with your friends.

Mostly Ds:

You are creative and independent, and you are a talented artist. You will most enjoy keeping your thoughts in a sketchbook. Let your innermost feelings inspire you to create emo poetry, beautiful art, and hilarious doodles.

Now try out the suggested diary format for your personality. If you love it, you've found your match! However, if it's not the best fit, try the others and select the one you're most comfortable with. GOOD LUCK ☺!

What are some of the things you've only said inside
your head, but that you've thought about saying to:
1. Your BFFs?

2. Someone at school who isn't always supernice
to you?

3. Your crush?

Tip Three: FIND A COMFY SPOT
AND CHILLAX AS YOU WRITE

Where would you choose for your secret diary-writing
hideout?

ME, IN MY
SECRET →
DIARY-WRITING HIDEOUT!

Draw a picture of yourself writing in your diary in your secret hideout.

OMG, NIKKI! YOU'RE WRITING IN A DIARY? CAN I READ IT?

OH, THIS? IT'S JUST A . . . BOOK I GOT FROM MY DOCTOR ON, UM . . . TOENAIL ODOR.

If someone caught you writing in your diary, what would you say to trick them? Write four different responses below:

HEY! IS THAT YOUR DIARY?!

WOW! So, that's it!

It's been so cool sharing my dorky world with you and also giving you a peek at some of my secret diary entries! I really hope you've liked my guide to being a dork and that you feel ready to go out into the world and spread the dorky word!

And don't forget the most important thing . . .
ALWAYS LET YOUR INNER DORK SHINE THROUGH!
Your dorkalicous friend,

Nikki Maxwell

squeee!

DO YOU HAVE WHAT IT TAKES
TO BECOME
A DORKETTE?

☐ Are you **obsessed** with Nikki Maxwell and her not—so—fabulous life?

☐ Do you say 'Squeee' in every other sentence?

☐ Do you **doodle** all over your school books?

If your answers are YES then
you could be one of our ten

DORK superfans
– aka **DORK**ettes –
tasked with spreading the love for
the adorable *Dork Diaries* series!

As a Dorkette you'll be the first to read the latest **DORK DIARIES** books, the first to receive exclusive content and the first to hear the latest dork-tastic news. Plus, you'll have access to an EXCLUSIVE Dorkette Facebook page enabling you to share your reviews, photos, competitions and Dorky tips with other Dork fans.

Visit
www.dorkdiaries.co.uk/dorkettes
for more details and tell us in less than 150 words why YOU should be crowned a Dorkette.

Our ten winners will also receive an **aDORKable** goodie bag!

What would YOU do
if the whole world
just stopped?

Yes. The WHOLE WORLD. Birds in the
air. Planes in the sky. And every
single person on the planet -
except you!

Because that's what keeps happening
to Hamish Ellerby...

Read on for a sneak preview
of Hamish's adventure in this
EXCLUSIVE extract from

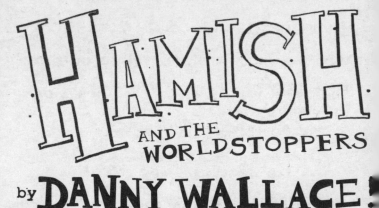

HAMISH
AND THE
WORLDSTOPPERS
by DANNY WALLACE!

Hamish tumbled to the ground, grazing his knees and rolling over until he went slap-bang into a fence. His bike skittered and clanked to the ground. The shopping went everywhere.

'Are you all right?'

He looked up to see a girl about his age. She was wearing blue combat trousers and a blue military jumper. She had a bag over her shoulder with the letters 'PPP' written across it and a small badge stuck to one side – a badge with the St. Autumnal's school sign on it. And, strangely, she had one blue streak through her otherwise jet-black hair.

'I'm fine,' said Hamish, looking around, panicked. He had nowhere to go and Grenville would be here any second. 'I'm sorry, I'm. . .'

'HA! HAHAHAHA!'

The laugh was loud and ~~malavolunt~~ evil.

Grenville was here. He dropped his bike to the ground. His associates did the same. The three boys each cracked their knuckles menacingly.

They had Hamish right where they wanted him. Up against a wall and just out of earshot of any nosey grown-ups, busybodies or blotter-jotters who might stop them undertaking their evil deeds.

Grenville sauntered forward, still in his El Gamba mask. Evidently, he thought he looked pretty cool in that.

Either side of him, Lurgie and Roger seemed to grow taller.

'Get up . . .' said Grenville, putting his hands on his hips. 'Get up right now—'

'Excuse me,' said the girl, interrupting. 'Why are you wearing a mask?'

'What?' said Grenville, who really didn't want to be distracted right now.

'Is it for dramatic effect?' she asked. 'Only you look like a doofus.'

Roger and Lurgie were shocked. Who was this girl? No one spoke to Grenville like this!

'I'll have you know this is a Mexican wrestling mask,' said Grenville, patiently. 'The same one worn by . . .

El Gamba!'

He made an impressive face. The girl scrunched up her nose.

'My cousin lives in Spain,' she said. 'Doesn't "El Gamba" mean . . . the Prawn?'

'What? No!'

'Yes it does,' said the girl, '"El Gamba" means "the prawn"'. What kind of name is the Prawn? The Prawn is pretty much the least frightening name of all time.'

'No it's not,' said Grenville, who felt like he was losing some of his power here. 'Shut up.'

'Oh, no, the Prawn, the Prawn!' she said, sarcastically. 'Well, I better do what you say, seeing as you're known as the Prawn and all. I wouldn't want to get light-to-moderate food poisoning or anything.'

Roger laughed. Lurgie pushed him to tell him to stop, then had to wipe his hand.

'Look, I'm pretty busy here,' said Grenville.

'Sorry,' said the girl. 'I must remember not to be so *shellfish.'*

Roger laughed again and even Lurgie had to admit that was a pretty good gag. *Who was this girl?* wondered Hamish.

'*Now, Ellerby,*' said Grenville, firmly. 'You need to be

punished for what you did to my associates.'

'I didn't do anything to your associates,' said Hamish, who felt a little braver with this girl around. 'Honestly. They just ran at me and missed.'

'Scratch and Mole said you made them look stupid in front of everybody,' said Grenville. 'And so now I'm afraid you must pay.'

The three boys were very close to poor Hamish now. He took a deep breath, ready for whatever they had in store. Grenville suddenly took Hamish's hand, lifted it up to eye level and said . . . 'Now *that's* a nice watch.'

'It's my dad's,' said Hamish. 'Or it was. Please, Grenville, look—'

'Well, if it was your dad's, it's not like he needs it now, is it?'

Hamish started to panic. He wanted to fight them. He could feel his chest tightening with rage. This was so unfair. And they were going to take the one special thing Hamish had.

But there were three of them. And they were so much bigger than him.

'I'll just borrow it, I think,' said Grenville, pulling the watch off Hamish's wrist and tossing it casually to Roger. 'I could do with a nice new watch.'

'Leave him alone,' said the girl. 'You're a bully in a mask. The only thing you've got in common with a prawn is the size of your brain.'

Oh, don't make this worse, thought Hamish.

'I bet you've never punched anybody in your life,' she said. 'I bet you'd just hurt your knuckles if you did!'

What was this girl doing? Why was she winding Grenville up?

'Oh, yeah?' said Grenville, smiling. 'Well, Hamish, prepare to find out. . .'

And as the nasty little thug raised one chubby fist to do just that . . . and as Hamish cursed that strange girl and closed his eyes in anticipation . . .

A bright . . .

. . . brilliant . . .

Hamish took in the scene around him.

Grenville with his fist in the air. Roger about to wipe his nose. Lurgie with his hands on his hips. The girl with the blue streak watching it all take place.

He began to laugh, out of nothing but sheer relief!

Twice the pause had saved him now!

Oh, thank you! Thank you!

He could do anything he wanted now. He could tweak Grenville's nose if he liked. He could kick Lurgie in the shin. He could swap everything in Roger's pockets around so he didn't know where anything was any more. He could pull down his pants and show them his bottom if he wanted to.

Hamish had the power.

Hamish had the control.

Hamish was the greatest force in the universe!

But what Hamish wasn't banking on was this.

The most awful, horrible, blood-curdling noise. . .

A noise so awful, so horrible and so blood-curdling it is impossible to tell you exactly what it sounded like.

Except that it was awful.

And horrible.

And it could curdle your blood.

A kind of

FVAAAAAAAAAAAAAAR!

A sort of

PHWAAEEEEEEEEEEEEER!

A type of

PHEFFVVAAAEEEEEEER!

It was the sound of pain and fear. Of nightmares. Of hope disappearing down a screaming plughole.

The noise was everywhere, almost like it was solid. It ran through Hamish's body, making his teeth ring. It was sharp and spiked and almost too loud to handle.

He raised his hands to his ears to block it out, but it was no good. The noise was stronger than he was.

Looking around him, he saw the sky darken – how was this possible, when the world was still? This had never happened in the other Pauses. Suddenly it wasn't so great to be the only one moving around. He wanted to ask questions, to talk to the others . . . which was when he heard something else.

A roar.

The terrifying clatter of hooves.

Hundreds of hooves.

The whispers, growing louder by the second.

The hum of a huge and approaching horde!

Hamish began to feel very frightened indeed. He wanted to run. To hide. To get inside somewhere, anywhere. He wanted to be in his own room more than anything in the world. He wanted his mum. He wanted his dad.

What was coming? What was round the corner?

These were questions Hamish would quickly realise he actually did **not** want the answers to.

Because the truth was so much worse than anything he could imagine.

Want to know what's
got Hamish so spooked?
Then make sure you look out for

HAMISH
AND THE WORLDSTOPPERS

by **DANNY WALLACE**

Out 12th of March!

Go to **worldofhamish.co.uk**
NOW to find out more about
Hamish and Danny, join the PDF,
watch exclusive videos PLUS
the chance to enter a special
competition to win Hamish
goodies and get YOUR name in
the next Hamish adventure!